WISDOM

of

FROGS

© 2008 by Moseley Road Inc.

This 2008 edition published by Metro Books,
by arrangement with Moseley Road Inc.

Art Director: Gus Yoo
Designer: Latricia Watford
Editor: Franchesca Ho Sang
Photo Researcher: Benjamin DeWalt

Metro Books
122 Fifth Avenue
New York, NY 10011

ISBN: 978-1-4351-0532-4

Printed and bound in China

3   5   7   9   10   8   6   4   2

WISDOM

of

FROGS

Compiled by
Franchesca Ho Sang

METRO BOOKS
NEW YORK

"Small opportunities are often the beginning of great enterprises."

–Demosthenes

"As we **grow** as unique persons, we learn to **respect** the **uniqueness** of others."

–*Robert H. Schuller*

"Don't fear change, embrace it."

-*Anthony J. D'Angelo*

"Don't try to walk
before you crawl."

–*Proverb*

"There is always
a smile
behind a tear."

–Helen Luecke

"The commonest thing is **delightful**
if one only hides it."
–*Oscar Wilde*

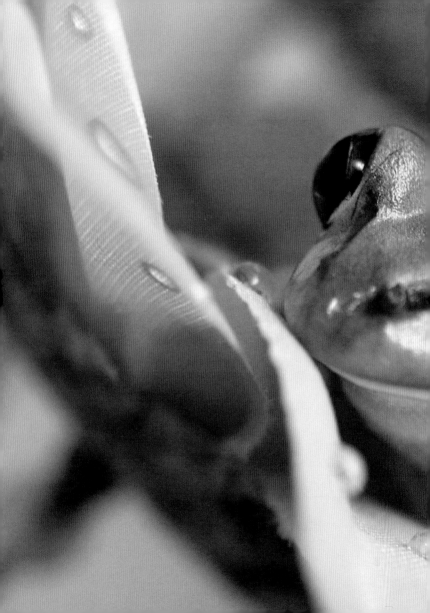

"This very **moment** is the seed from which tomorrow's **happiness grows.**"

–*Margaret Lindsey*

"**Stand up**
for what is right,
even if
you are standing
alone."

—Anonymous

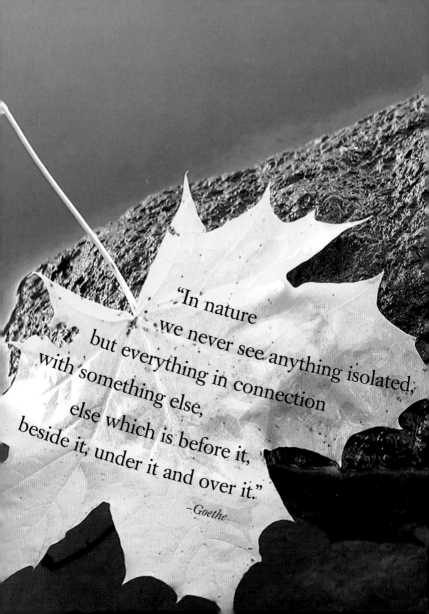

"In nature
we never see anything isolated,
but everything in connection
with something else,
else which is before it,
beside it, under it and over it."

–*Goethe*

"Let your **life** lightly dance on the edges of Time like dew on the tip of a leaf."

–Rabindranath Tagore

"One mustn't **criticize** other people on grounds where he can't stand perpendicular himself."

–*Mark Twain*

"Do not be **too hard**, lest you be **broken**; do not be **too soft**, lest you be **squeezed**."

–Ali ibn Abi Talib

"Wisdom is oft times nearer when we stoop than when we soar."

–William Wordsworth

"Truth
is the property
of no individual
but is the **treasure**
of **all men**."

–*Ralph Waldo Emerson*

"For here we are **not afraid** to **follow truth** wherever it may lead."

–Thomas Jefferson

"Above all, watch with glittering eyes
the whole world around,
because the **greatest secrets**
are always hidden
in the most **unlikely places**."

–*Roald Dahl*

"Without **courage, wisdom** bears **not** fruit."

–Baltasar Gracian

"Keep your eyes
on the stars,
but remember
to keep your feet
on the ground."

–*Theodore Roosevelt*

"Courage is the power to let go of the familiar."

–Raymond Lindquist

"You can **steer** yourself in **any direction** you **choose**."

–Dr. Seuss

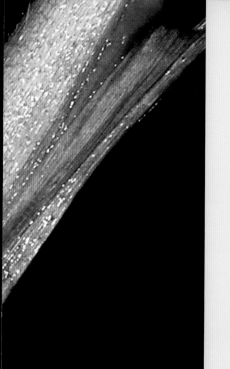

"Stop trying to
fit in
when you were
born to
stand out."

–Anonymous

"Success is a ladder
that cannot be climbed
with your hands in your pocket."

–*American proverb*

"Each **difficult** moment has the **potential** to **open my eyes** and **open my heart.**"

–Myla Kabat-Zinn

"None, but people of strong passion are capable of rising **to greatness.**"

–*Comte de Mirabeau*

"**Genius,**
the power which dazzles human eyes
is often but
perseverance in **disguise.**"

–*Mike Newlin*

"Man cannot
aspire
if he looked down;
if he **rise**,
he must look up."

–Samuel Smiles

"The only people who never tumble are those who never mount the high wire."

–Oprah Winfrey

"When it is
darkest,
men see the
stars."

–Ralph Waldo Emerson

"For the wise man looks into space and he **knows** there is no **limited dimensions.**"

–Lao Tzu

"Enjoy the honey-heavy dew of slumber."

–*Shakespeare*

"**Fear** doesn't exist
anywhere
except in the mind."

–Dale Carnegie

"**Deep** into that
darkness peering,
long I stood there wondering,
fearing, Doubting,
dreaming dreams
no mortal ever dared
to **dream** before."

–Edgar Allan Poe

"The **ultimate measure** of a man
is not where he stands
in moments of **comfort**
and **convenience**,
but where he stands
at times of **challenge** and
controversy…"

–*Martin Luther King Jr.*

"One sees **great things** from the valley; only small things from the **peak**."

–*G.K. Chesterton*

"He who would search for pearls must dive below."

–John Dryden

"Sometimes you have to **let go** to see if there was anything **worth holding onto.**"

–*Anonymous*

"Refuse to be **average**.
Let your **heart soar**
as **high** as it will."

–A.W. Tozer

"In order to **please others,**
we **lose** our hold
on our life's **purpose.**"

–*Epictetus*

"**Never frown**
because you never
know who
is falling in **love**
with your **smile**."

–*Anonymous*

"Out of **suffering** have emerged the **strongest** souls; the most massive characters are seared with scars."

–Kahlil Gibran

"The grass is **always** greener on the **other** side of the fence."

–*Proverb*

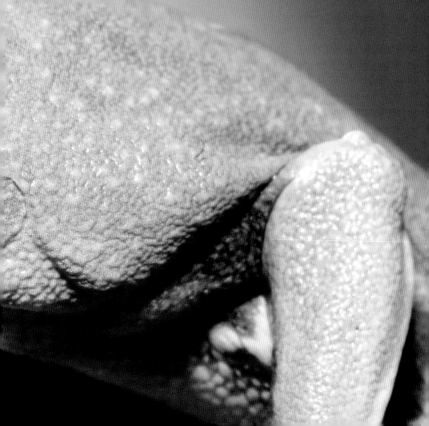

"To **succeed**
you need to find something to **hold on** to,
something to **motivate** you,
something to **inspire** you."

–*Tony Dorsett*

"There's not enough darkness **in all the world** to put out the light of even one small candle."

–*Robert Alden*

"Open your arms to change,

but don't let go of your **values.**"

–*Dalai Lama*

"A **hero** is
one who knows how to **hang on**
one minute longer."

—Norwegian proverb

"Better a **diamond** with a flaw than a pebble without."

–*Confucious*

"Tough times
never last,
but tough
people do."

–Robert H. Schuller

"When **fortune** calls,

offer her a chair." —*Yiddish proverb*

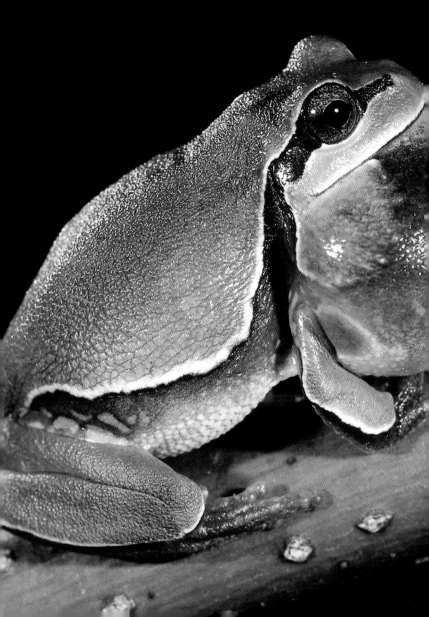

"Conceit
may **puff**
a man **up**,
but never
prop him up."

—John Ruskin

"Some people
make things happen,
some
watch things happen,
while others wonder
what has happened."

–Proverb

"When
you want to marry a
PRINCE
you will have to kiss many frogs."
–Dutch proverb

"A sense of **curiosity** is nature's original school of **education**."

–*Smiley Blarton*

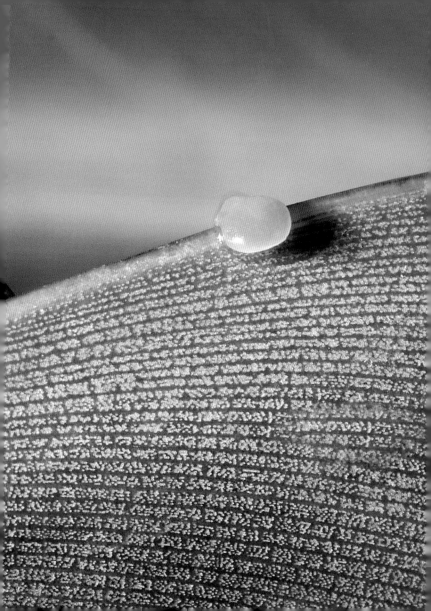

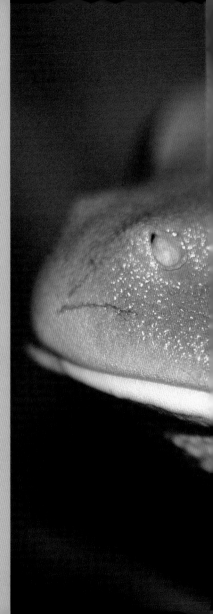

"The way to
see by Faith
is to shut the
Eye of Reason."

–*Benjamin Franklin*

"**Seeking** and searching, I have found my **own home**, deep within my **own being**."

–*Sri Guru Granth Sahib*

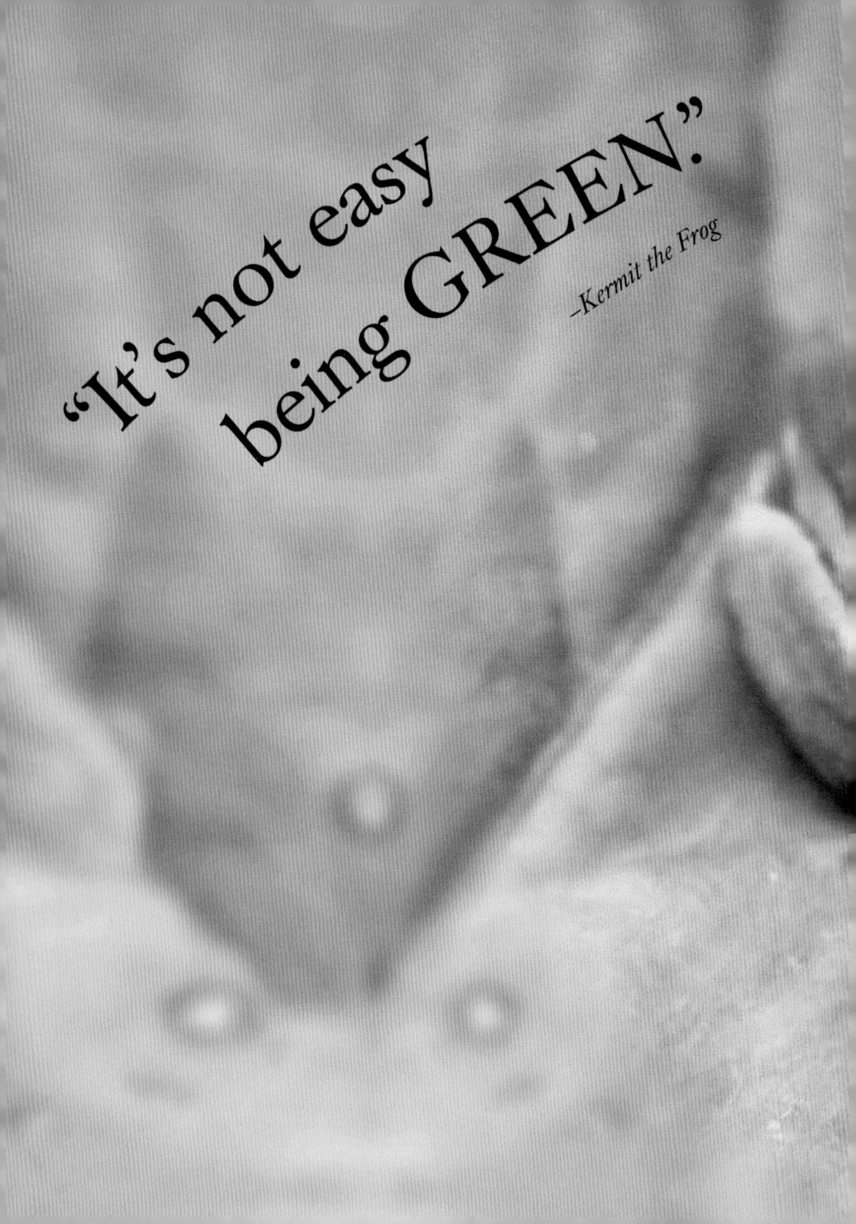
"It's not easy
being GREEN."
–Kermit the Frog

"Our way
is **not soft grass,**
it's a mountain
path with lots of
rocks. But it goes
upwards, forward,
toward the **sun.**"

–Dr. Ruth Westheimer

"A single rose can be my garden ..."

a single friend, my world."

–Leo Buscaglia

PICTURE CREDITS